For Levi and Quinn
and all the others

www.mascotbooks.com

Air Force Ace

For more information, please contact:
Mascot Books
620 Herndon Parkway, Suite 320
Herndon, VA 20170
info@mascotbooks.com

Library of Congress Control Number: 2019909400

CPSIA Code: PRT0120A
ISBN-13: 978-1-64543-047-6

Printed in the United States

AIR FORCE
ACE

Katie Marcucci

Illustrated by Junica

Ace was a dog. A smart dog. For days he sensed something important was happening in his house, but he couldn't quite figure out just what. Early the next morning, it became clear.

With the sun still in bed behind the fading stars, Ace was awakened by the sound of his daddy stacking suitcases by the front door. His large work bags were packed full and bursting at the seams. Ace had seen this before.

He remembered the last time those bags were packed. Mommy told him Daddy was leaving for a "deployment," which meant he'd be away from them for many, many days. He wouldn't be home at dinner time to play with him or to kiss Ace goodnight.

More than anything, what Ace really remembered was how much he missed Daddy. All of this made Ace sad, but he knew deployments didn't last forever. Just like last time, Daddy always came back.

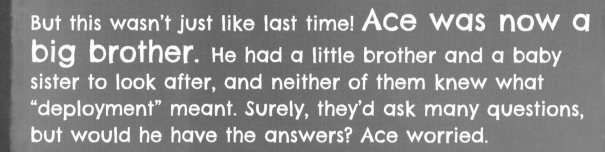

But this wasn't just like last time! Ace was now a big brother. He had a little brother and a baby sister to look after, and neither of them knew what "deployment" meant. Surely, they'd ask many questions, but would he have the answers? Ace worried.

Ace watched Daddy set his last green bags by the door. He watched carefully as Daddy walked into Little Brother's and Baby Sister's bedrooms, knowing he was kissing them goodbye. Then Ace felt a final pat on his furry head and sat next to Mommy's feet as she hugged Daddy tightly. It was at that moment Ace decided he had to know more.

Ace was determined to discover the answers to the questions he knew Little Brother would have, to know what to say to Mommy and Baby Sister on days when they were missing Daddy. He had to find out what this thing called "deployment" was. After all, he was the dog of the house.

While Mommy and Daddy were still holding each other, Ace quietly crawled into Daddy's final suitcase. Soon he heard the zipper close him in and felt himself being wheeled out the door. It might have been scary, **but Ace was a brave dog!**

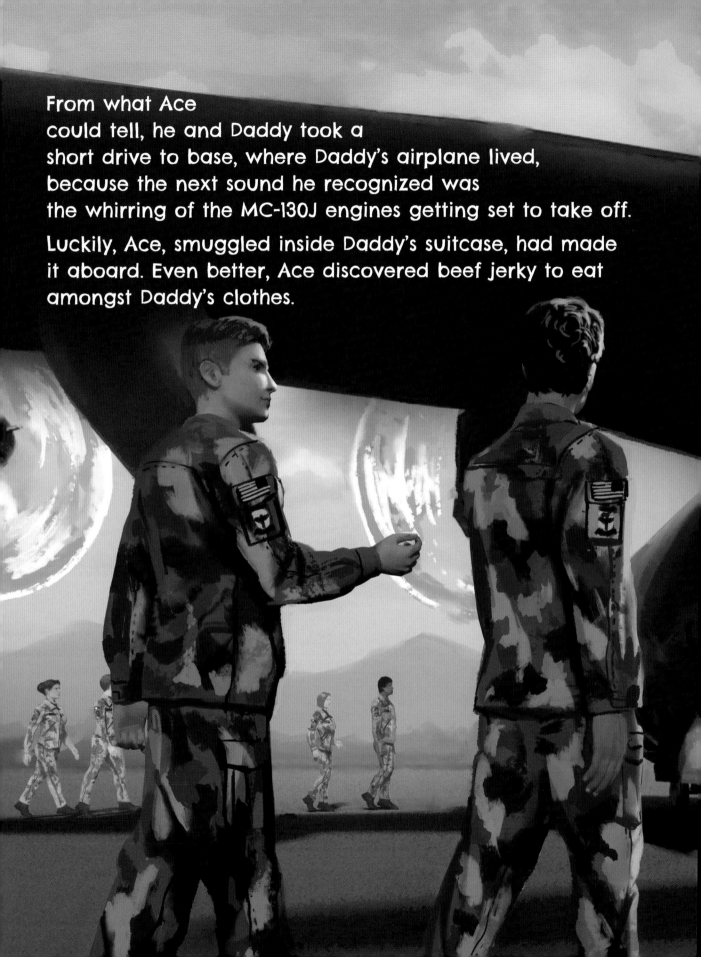

From what Ace
could tell, he and Daddy took a
short drive to base, where Daddy's airplane lived,
because the next sound he recognized was
the whirring of the MC-130J engines getting set to take off.

Luckily, Ace, smuggled inside Daddy's suitcase, had made
it aboard. Even better, Ace discovered beef jerky to eat
amongst Daddy's clothes.

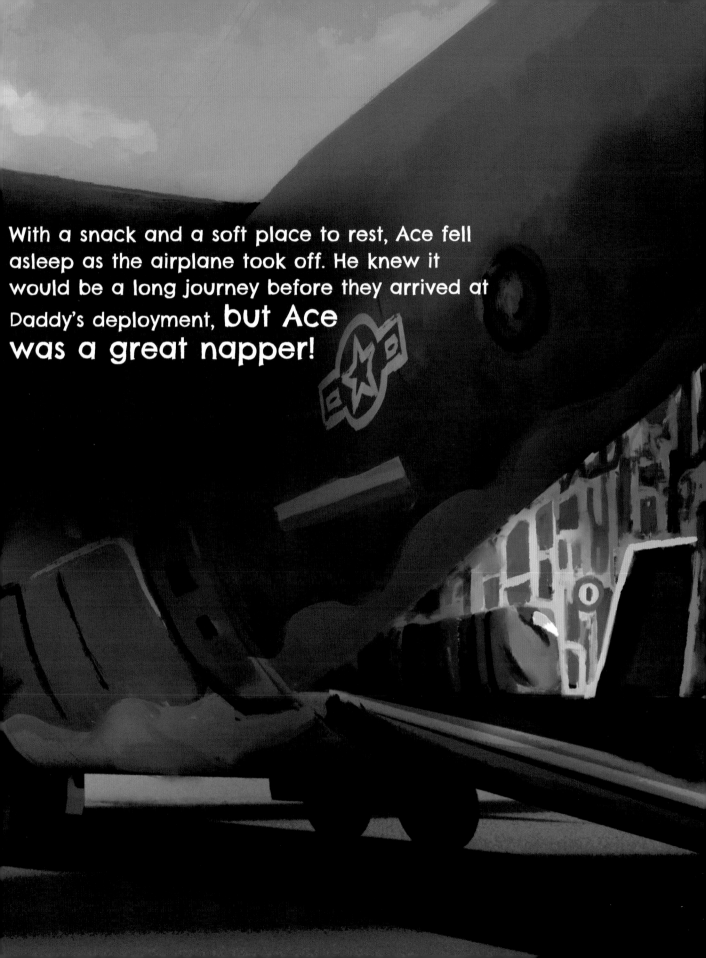

With a snack and a soft place to rest, Ace fell asleep as the airplane took off. He knew it would be a long journey before they arrived at Daddy's deployment, **but Ace was a great napper!**

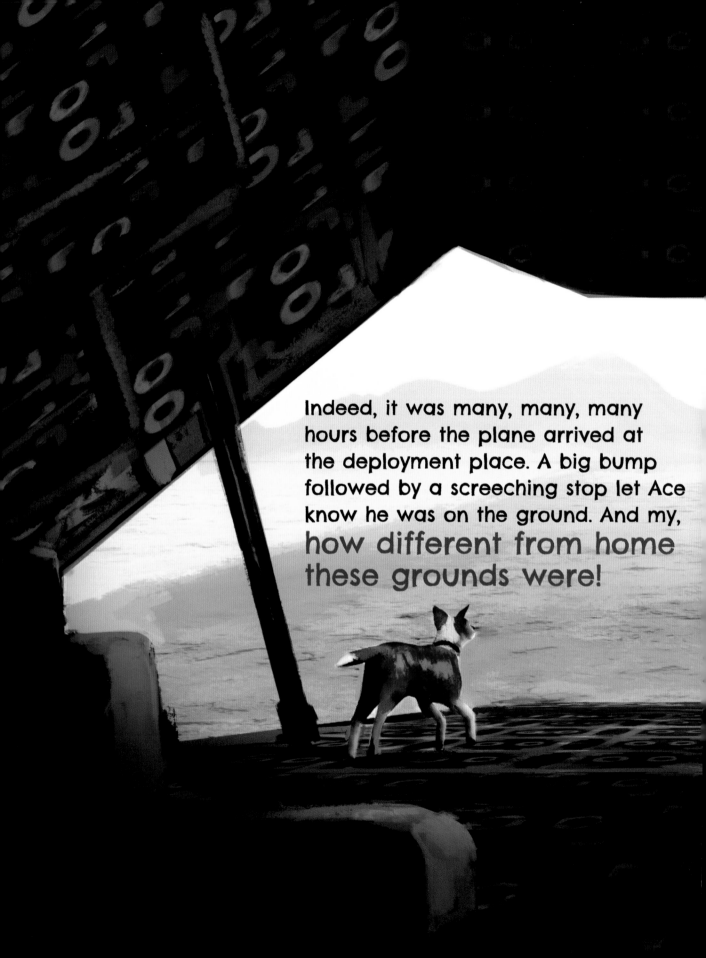

Indeed, it was many, many, many hours before the plane arrived at the deployment place. A big bump followed by a screeching stop let Ace know he was on the ground. And my, **how different from home these grounds were!**

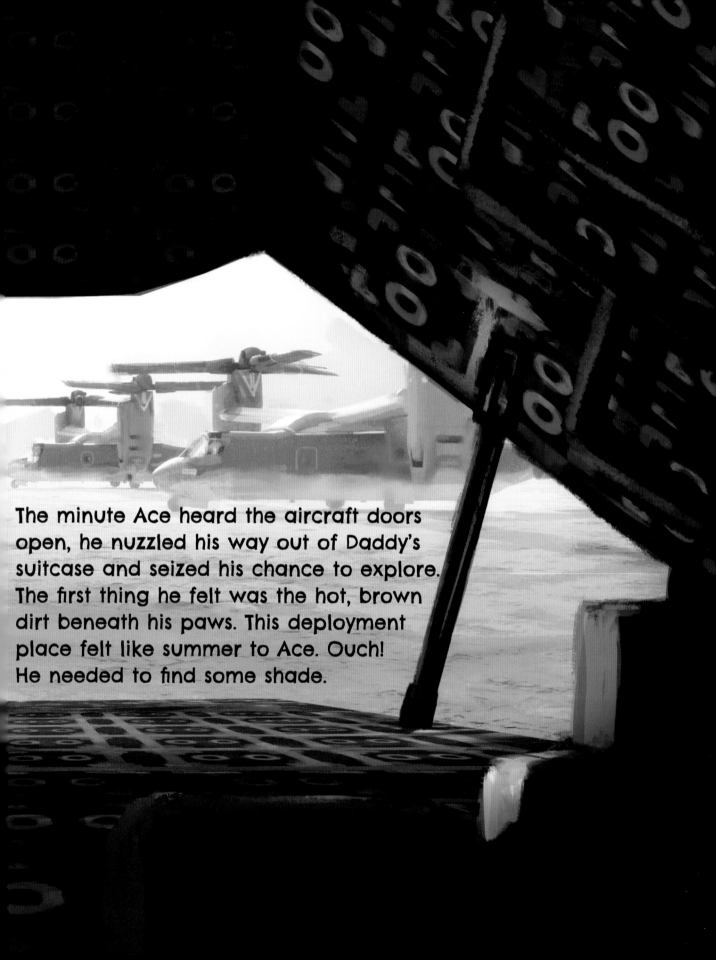

The minute Ace heard the aircraft doors open, he nuzzled his way out of Daddy's suitcase and seized his chance to explore. The first thing he felt was the hot, brown dirt beneath his paws. This deployment place felt like summer to Ace. Ouch! He needed to find some shade.

Ace followed his nose to the nearest building, which happened to be giving off delicious smells, too. Poking his head inside, Ace knew he had found the chow hall, where all the airmen ate their food together like a big family. He recognized the scents of spicy tacos, cheesy lasagna, juicy hamburgers, and even scarfed up some crispy bacon that had been dropped.

Deployment had all the meals
Daddy enjoyed at home, even
ice cream! Ace could hardly believe his eyes when he saw an
airman eating a chocolate ice cream cone. There was lots of
chatter, too. Everyone was busy talking, laughing, and telling
stories. Ace was happy to know Daddy was in a place with
good food and happy friends.

Ace's ears perked up when he heard an airman ask another if he was ready to play. Ace loved to play! He was amazed and thought, *I'm definitely following them.* He tagged along behind the two airmen, soon finding himself amongst many more.

On an outside court, he saw a large group of people playing basketball. Others were lifting weights nearby, tossing a football, or jogging around a dusty track. Ace was learning the importance of exercise during deployment, and it brought him comfort to know Daddy was staying healthy while he was away.

Ace joined in running the rings of the track like he and Daddy often did together at home. It felt wonderful to stretch his legs after the long trip. But afterwards, Ace grew tired, and he knew he had to find a soft place to rest. It had been quite the journey. His paws turned toward a row of darkened, quiet buildings nearby, perhaps the perfect place to rest.

And indeed it was! Ace found himself in a room with row after row of beds. They weren't fancy, but they sure looked inviting. As he wandered the room, he saw many photos of happy families next to each bedside; laughing children hugging smiling parents, mommies and daddies holding babies, and lots of happy dogs next to their favorite airman. One bed looked and smelled particularly inviting. Ace could not help but curl up on its pillow. He was very talented at sleeping and was snoring away in the blink of an eye.

Ace had no idea how long he'd been asleep, but his eyes opened immediately at the sweet sound of a most familiar voice.

"Ace! How can it be you're lying here on my bed?" he heard Daddy exclaim. Ace didn't answer the question but rather gave Daddy hundreds of kisses. How happy he was to see his dad!

Daddy, in turn, looked concerned. "Ace, I'm so glad to see you," he said, stroking his fur. "I love you so much, and whenever I'm away, you can't imagine how much I miss you and our family. But a deployment is not where you should be."

Ace looked a little hurt.

Daddy continued to explain, "Deployments are very busy, with lots of helping to do. Sometimes that means we work long hours, use heavy equipment made for grown-ups only, or even travel to distant places for a few days. We wouldn't have anywhere to play together, and you would be very bored waiting for me. Here, let me show you."

Ace stayed right by Daddy's side as they exited the barracks, returning to the hot dirt and bright sun. The whirring sounds of airplane engines grew louder as Ace and Daddy walked closer to the flight line. Daddy pointed out, "Over there is my aircraft, Ace. The mighty MC-130J."

Ace instantly recognized its four propellers. The back of the aircraft was open, and small vehicles with large crates were zipping in and out. "My friends are working hard to load food and water so we can share it with those in nearby villages who are thirsty and hungry," explained Daddy.

Pointing again, he continued, "Over there is a CV-22, ready to deliver books and school supplies for local children. And in the distance, a C-17 is coming in for landing with more helpers on board ready to get these and other jobs done."

Ace could see it was busy, hard, important work. He was sure proud of Daddy and the good he was doing on deployment.

Daddy knelt down next to Ace and whispered, "Thank you for loving me, Ace, as I love you. At the same time, I need you to go home to Mommy and Little Brother and Baby Sister. You can tell them I am safe and happy and healthy because you have seen and smelled it yourself." Ace's tail wagged away! He was sad to leave Daddy but glad to share this new information with his family.

When the next aircraft returning home from deployment departed, Ace was on it, curled up next to other airmen who were done being helpers and excited to return home. Indeed, when the long journey ended and Ace jumped into the arms of his awaiting Mommy, he felt so much love and joy.

Ace looked forward to the day when Daddy would step off that same plane and into his family's arms. In the meantime, they would miss him, but Mommy, Little Brother, Baby Sister, and Ace would all take care of each other.

About the Author

Born and raised in Oregon, Katie Marcucci's life as a United States Air Force spouse has taken her all around the world. As the mother of two, her focus has been to make "home" wherever the family lands.

Katie is a graduate of Oregon State University, where she met her husband. She is an avid runner, certified yoga instructor, and published author. Above all, she is an example to her children to bloom wherever you are planted.

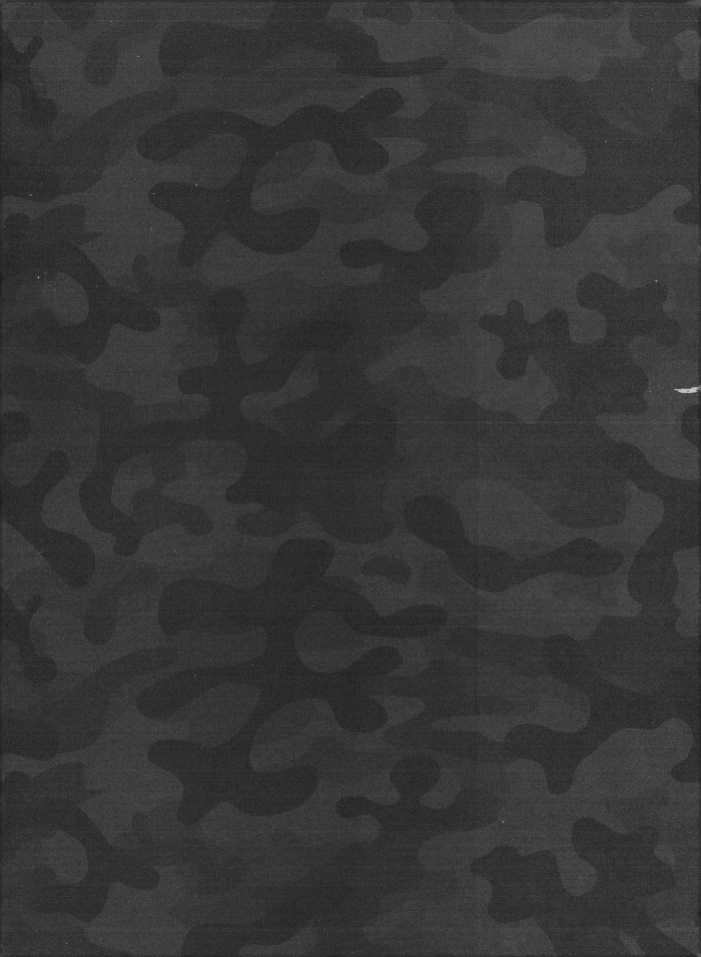